A day at the Colosseum

The adventures of Mark, who goes back in time. He spends one day in the Colosseum during the games given in honour of the emperor Trajan ... 1900 years ago.

Hello, my name is Mark and I want to tell you about all the incredible things that happened to me when I was at the Colosseum. We were on holiday near Rome in Italy and on my tenth birthday I went with my father to see the Colosseum. The train, the tram, the bus, one hour queuing. So many people. Sure, I enjoyed the visit, but at a certain point I lost my father. I went all around the square. There were funny people dressed as roman soldiers and guards, and I stopped every now and then to have a look, but my father was nowhere to be seen. So I sat down in front of one of the arches.

And then … when I wake up, everything has changed. Everything all around me looks new, even the steps I am sitting on are of white stone, the square is all tiled with big slabs of stone, and right in front of me there is an enormous statue of gold; a bit like the statue of liberty, but all gold, with rays around its head and a ball in its hand. It is the statue of a pagan God, I've gone back to roman times!

Just as I was about to stand up and look around, a strange little man appears. He is dressed in a sheet and is in the company of a girl. She's also draped in robes. They look like something out of one of those reliefs that you see in the museums. The boy says something, but I understand practically nothing. They seem okay, just a little strange, but from the look on their faces, I see that they are thinking I'm the strange one. They invite me to follow them, and we go all together towards the Roman Forum, where there is a lot of confusion. Great!!

We walk along a beautifully smooth street, which leads us in between high white walls; everywhere there are columns and flights of steps. The street is very crowded; everybody is in a hurry and keep pushing us, until we arrive in a wide square, full of statues and columns, and surrounded by magnificent palaces and temples.

The little boy suddenly pushes me through a narrow passage. His name is Julius, and his sister's name, if I understood correctly, is Fausta. We are now under a colonnade, and Julius makes signals that can only mean: stay quiet. I don't say anything as he wouldn't understand me anyway.

"Trajanus imperator" - Julius whispers - and then I realise that the man in the red cloak must be the actual emperor. Trajan is talking to a man, and from what I understood later on, he is deciding about the grand festival he wants to have organised to celebrate his victory. Trajan and his army won a long war against the Dacians and my dad says they lived where Rumania is today. There were gold mines there, so they brought back an enormous war booty, and now can afford a big feast called triumph, complete with games in the Colosseum.

From behind a column I can see Trajan, sitting comfortably while some men, ceremoniously dressed in white robes, branding swords and shields, line up in front of him.

They are the representatives of the senate and of the people. When they salute they raise their hand.

Trajan starts giving orders: the games have to be magnificent and splendid, and everybody must get to see them, at least for one day. Ten thousand gladiators must get ready to fight, and thousands of wild beasts have to be carried to Rome, from every province in the empire.

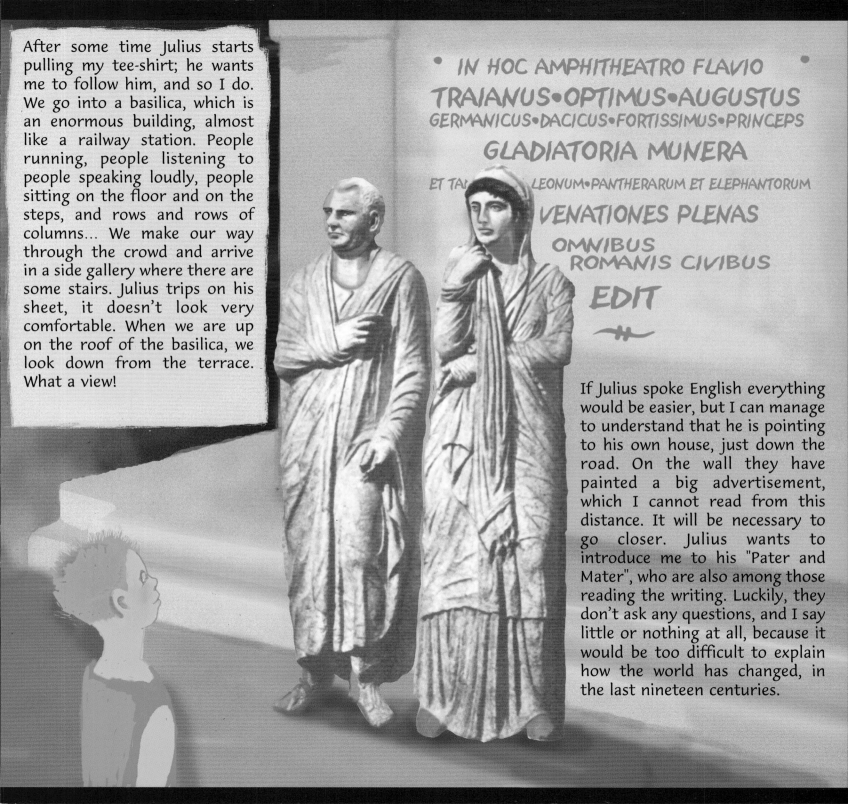

After some time Julius starts pulling my tee-shirt; he wants me to follow him, and so I do. We go into a basilica, which is an enormous building, almost like a railway station. People running, people listening to people speaking loudly, people sitting on the floor and on the steps, and rows and rows of columns… We make our way through the crowd and arrive in a side gallery where there are some stairs. Julius trips on his sheet, it doesn't look very comfortable. When we are up on the roof of the basilica, we look down from the terrace. What a view!

IN HOC AMPHITHEATRO FLAVIO
TRAIANUS·OPTIMUS·AUGUSTUS
GERMANICUS·DACICUS·FORTISSIMUS·PRINCEPS
GLADIATORIA MUNERA
ET TAN LEONUM·PANTHERARUM ET ELEPHANTORUM
VENATIONES PLENAS
OMNIBUS
ROMANIS CIVIBUS
EDIT

If Julius spoke English everything would be easier, but I can manage to understand that he is pointing to his own house, just down the road. On the wall they have painted a big advertisement, which I cannot read from this distance. It will be necessary to go closer. Julius wants to introduce me to his "Pater and Mater", who are also among those reading the writing. Luckily, they don't ask any questions, and I say little or nothing at all, because it would be too difficult to explain how the world has changed, in the last nineteen centuries.

It looks like I have come at the right moment. There will be fights in the Colosseum!

We rush back to the amphitheatre where, in the meantime, there is hustle and bustle everywhere. At the top there are hundreds of men who are pulling up some ropes, which are tied to big stone blocks. Julius says that it is the velarium. It is a circle made of wood and ropes, raised above the seats by many ropes . On top of the web of ropes the awning will be rolled out, to shelter the audience from the sun.
I tell Julius that I want to see the show, too, but he answers that children are not admitted. What? No children?!
It is absurd, there must be a way to sneak in. Julius' sister, Fausta, has an idea. The clothes are so wide that it's easy to hide. Especially as there will be a large crowd: 50.000 people can fit into the Colosseum. And there are 80 gates for all these people. There will be many guards, every entrance will be controlled, but in the confusion maybe nobody will notice two extra feet… who knows?
Tomorrow will be the great day. For one night I can sleep at Julius' house. What an adventure!

The following day, thanks to Julius' aunt we are among the first to get in the Colosseum. We can see almost nothing, and climb many stairs with very high steps. At last I sit down and look around, but .....

The balcony where I am is so high that I won't see anything. Not only that, there are only women around here. I don't think it is the right place to watch the fights. I can't see Julius, maybe he left his hiding place while we were climbing the stairs and now has found a good seat amidst the public.

I don't like it. In some way I must get down. Only, there are some guards at the doors and in the corridors who will surely arrest me. The ladies don't seem to notice my presence, so I decide to go straight from the gallery down to the men who are sitting lower down.

I slowly lower myself down from the banister, till I remain hanging from it. I let go and fall for at least one metre, but I don't hurt myself. It's like being in a movie. The ladies haven't moved, maybe they are fake. Down here, instead, there is such chaos. The men push and shout, somebody laughs weirdly, and just look at the faces! … A big, stinky man grabs my arm and start shouting something incomprehensible to another man.

I try to wriggle free, but he squeezes me even tighter and drags me with him through the crowd. Now everybody is staring at me and shouting something in my face. The guy pushes me towards one of the exits where the guards are standing. And then, just in time, another man punches him in the nose. First of all he becomes bright red, then he starts trembling with rage, and finally he lets go of me, to jump on top of his opponent. Fighting in the Colosseum.

In the meantime I run as fast as I can among the people, down the steps, to get as near as possible to the arena. Now nobody notices me, because the show is about to start. Drums are rolling: soldiers, horses, gladiators and trumpeters enter the arena. The gladiators are wearing splendid outfits; they stop in front of the emperor, who is still wearing his magnificent purple cloak. There is absolute silence. Then a sound of trumpets, and the whole audience stands up.

After the parade of the gladiators, here are the animals. All kinds of them: lions. tigers, leopards, a giraffe, two huge bears, a pair of zebras, a pair of elephants and even a crocodile. They walk around the arena, and the people cheer. Everybody laughs when the brown bear stands on his hind legs.

I have got down nearer the arena now, so I manage to see how the guards lead the animals, with long ropes. After the presentation, they are brought back to the cages, then they'll have to fight. Today, in only one day, almost one hundred animals will die.

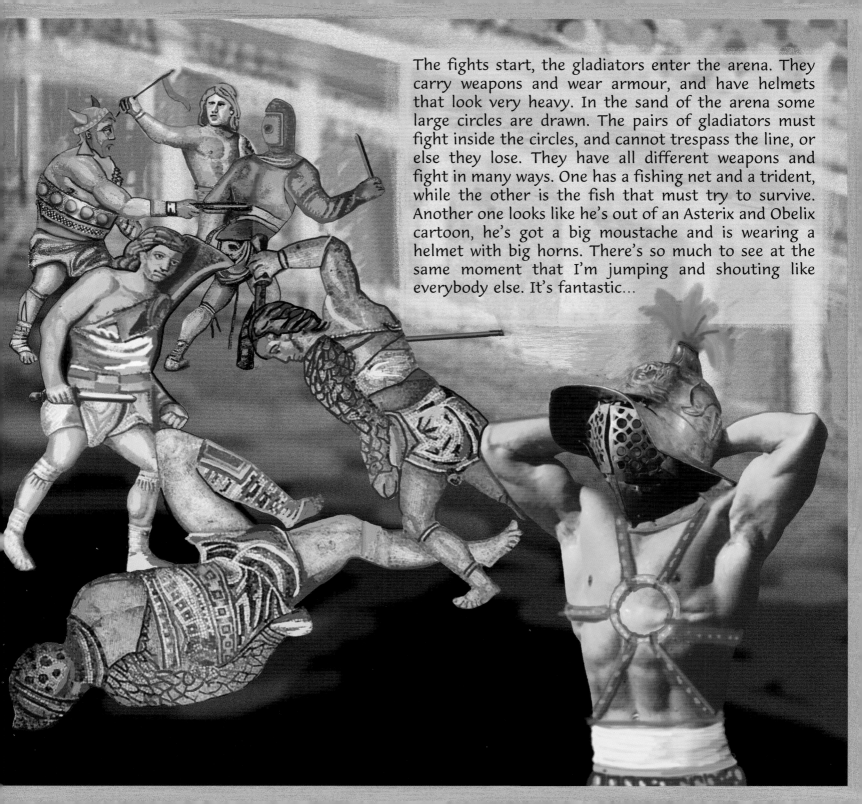

The fights start, the gladiators enter the arena. They carry weapons and wear armour, and have helmets that look very heavy. In the sand of the arena some large circles are drawn. The pairs of gladiators must fight inside the circles, and cannot trespass the line, or else they lose. They have all different weapons and fight in many ways. One has a fishing net and a trident, while the other is the fish that must try to survive. Another one looks like he's out of an Asterix and Obelix cartoon, he's got a big moustache and is wearing a helmet with big horns. There's so much to see at the same moment that I'm jumping and shouting like everybody else. It's fantastic…

The winners leave the field, flexing their muscles at the cheering crowd. In the middle of the arena big wooden trapdoors are opened, and a scenery is raised. Here is a bush, over there two palm trees and a little hill appear. Then, once again from trapdoors all around the arena, some cages are raised, and lions, tigers, panthers start coming out. While the beasts come up, they prod them with spears, so they get more agitated. The beasts run ,and leap on the men, who use a spear, so that they won't come too near. The animals lose a lot of blood, and the arena is all red.

It is a horrible show, and I would like to shout to stop it ...

After the pause, suddenly there is a great commotion: from the top of the amphitheatre thousands of wooden balls are being thrown down on the public. One of them falls on my head and it really hurts, surely I'll get a bump. But I have the ball in my hands. It opens, and inside there is a strip of metal with the image of something that looks like a sandal. But, before I can get a better look, somebody snatches my ball and shouts "I won!".

All around me people fight for the balls; with the right one you can win some nice prizes, even a horse. But the show is about to start again. An announcer takes a long time to explain what is going to happen, he says it's something historical: I hear it's Romulus against the Sabines, and suddenly two armies enter and line up in the arena. Then, when everybody is calmer, and is sitting in silence, the trumpets sound and the groups start to fight.

Two good-looking warriors have a duel, but the rest of it looks just like a massacre. After the first fight, the arena is quickly cleared, to make place for the next historical fight, which, this time, is more recent, being the battle of the Romans against the Dacians, the war that's just been won by Trajan.

The emperor represented in battle is actually there, in person on the imperial podium. The poor Dacians who didn't die in the war were taken prisoners and brought to Rome only to die later in a fake battle in the Colosseum. If I had seen all this on TV maybe I would have liked it, but seeing it so close up is too much. Too much of everything. Too cruel, too violent, too bloody.

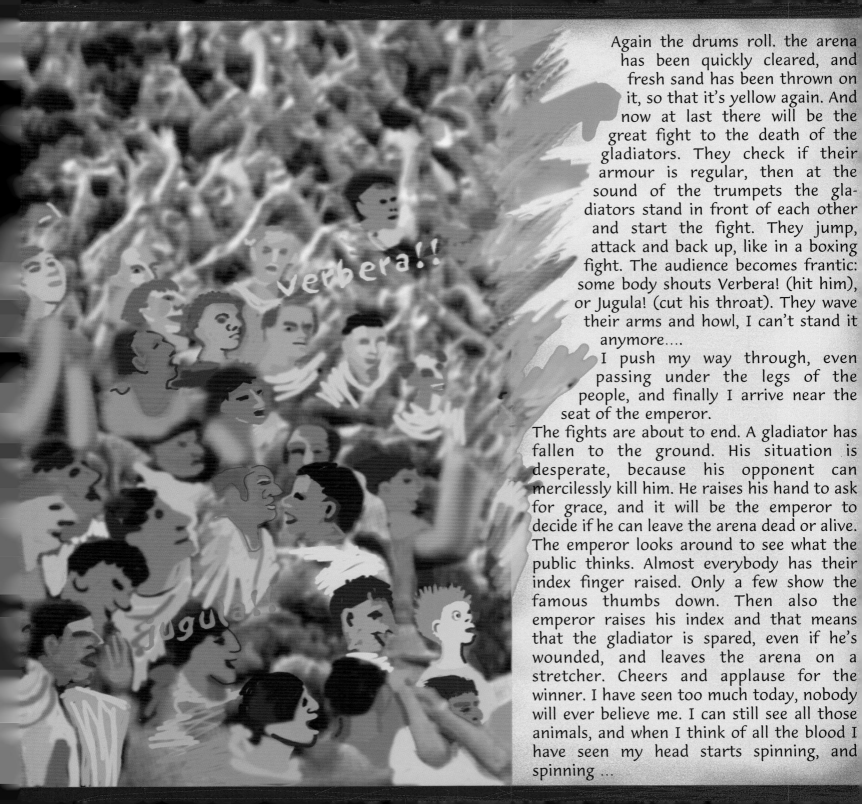

Again the drums roll. the arena has been quickly cleared, and fresh sand has been thrown on it, so that it's yellow again. And now at last there will be the great fight to the death of the gladiators. They check if their armour is regular, then at the sound of the trumpets the gladiators stand in front of each other and start the fight. They jump, attack and back up, like in a boxing fight. The audience becomes frantic: some body shouts Verbera! (hit him), or Jugula! (cut his throat). They wave their arms and howl, I can't stand it anymore....

I push my way through, even passing under the legs of the people, and finally I arrive near the seat of the emperor.

The fights are about to end. A gladiator has fallen to the ground. His situation is desperate, because his opponent can mercilessly kill him. He raises his hand to ask for grace, and it will be the emperor to decide if he can leave the arena dead or alive. The emperor looks around to see what the public thinks. Almost everybody has their index finger raised. Only a few show the famous thumbs down. Then also the emperor raises his index and that means that the gladiator is spared, even if he's wounded, and leaves the arena on a stretcher. Cheers and applause for the winner. I have seen too much today, nobody will ever believe me. I can still see all those animals, and when I think of all the blood I have seen my head starts spinning, and spinning ...

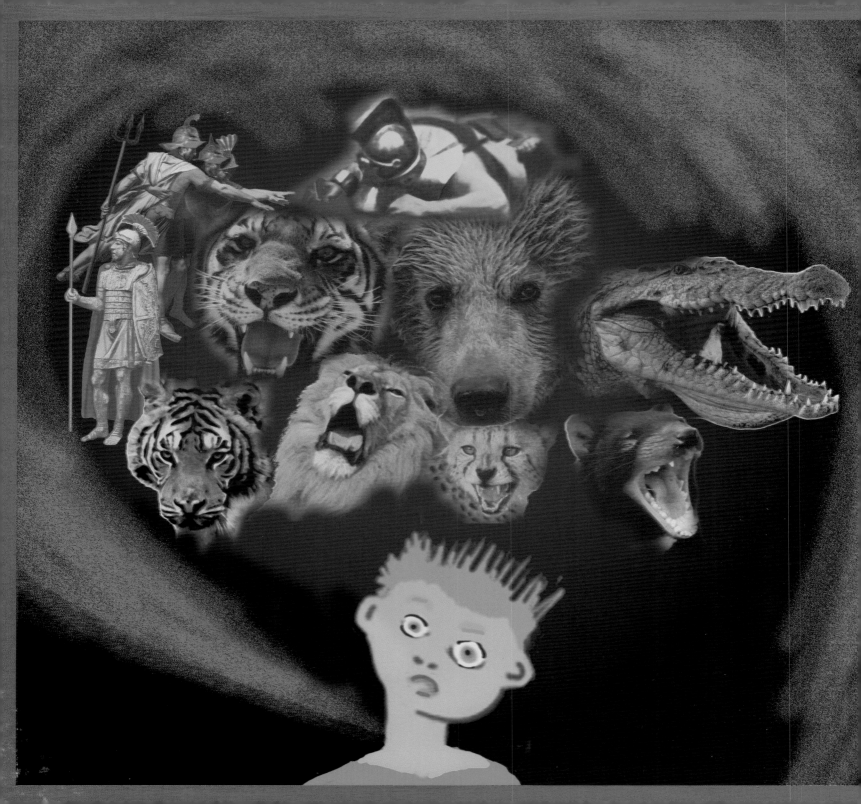

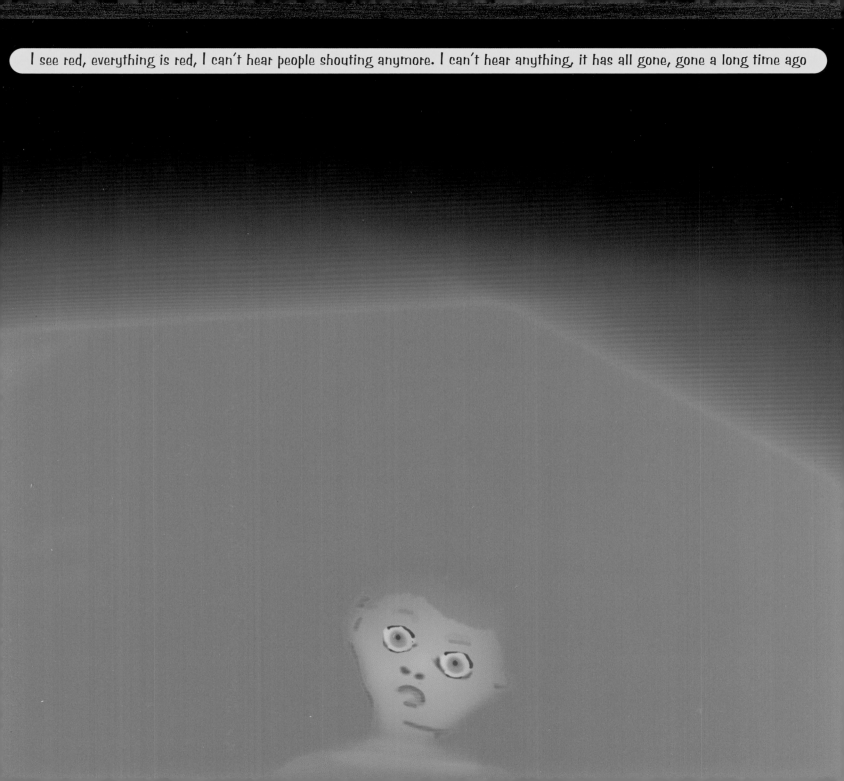